To Patti & Sul,

with much love at Christmas, 1983,

God Bless

Anne

CHRISTMAS
CHRISTMAS
BOX
W. McCONNELL. DELT

Wishing you the Season's Greetings.

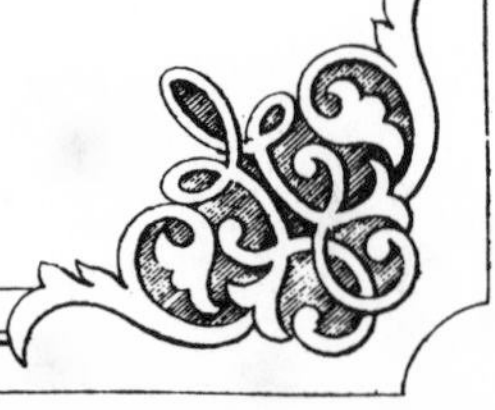

A VICTORIAN CHRISTMAS SONG BOOK

PRESENTED AND COMPILED BY

RICHARD GRAVES

M

TO DEAR MARY,
WHO HAS BEEN PATIENTLY
STUMBLING OVER PILES
OF DUSTY MUSIC FOR MOST
OF HER MARRIED LIFE.

Published 1980 by Macmillan London Ltd. London and Basingstoke.
Associated companies in Delhi, Dublin, Hong Kong, Johannesburg,
Lagos, Melbourne, New York, Singapore, Tokyo.

Created, designed and produced by Russel Sharp Limited,
9 Queen Street, Horsham, West Sussex, RH13 5AA

ISBN 0 333 306627

Phototypeset in Great Britain by SX Composing Limited, Rayleigh, Essex.
Printed in Spain by Printer industria gráfica sa
Sant Vicenç dels Horts Barcelona D.L.B. 18335-1980

CONTENTS

Preface 6

Piano Solo: A Christmas Holiday 13

Song: What shall we sing at Christmas? 16

Song: The Mistletoe Bough 19

Song: Song of the Robin Redbreast 23

Song: Winter Evergreens 30

Song: It was my Father's Custom 35

Piano Solo: Glad Tidings 37

Song: Now I've got no Daddy 40

Song: The Broken Slate 43

Song: One Touch of Nature makes the whole World kin 46

Song: Mother and the dear old Dad 49

Piano Solo: Christmas with the Old Folks 52

Song: Christmas 1874 55

Song: Christmas Boxes 57

Piano Solo: A Christmas Party 59

Song: Christmas Bells 67

Song: Miss Hooligan's Christmas Cake 71

Song: Santy Claus is comin' 'fore de Mornin' 74

Song: Under the Mistletoe 77

Monologue: A Christmas Pantomime 81

Piano Solo: The Pantomime Schottische 93

Piano Solo: A Winter Ride 96

Grand Symphonic Poem: The Kitchen Band 102

Musical Games and Puzzles 106

Piano Solo: New Year's Eve 108

Acknowledgments 111

PREFACE

HE feast of Christmas came late to the Victorian home; indeed many of the trappings that are now associated with this most sumptuous of celebrations, such as the exchanging of cards or bringing indoors an evergreen tree and hanging it with decorations, were themselves Victorian inventions or importations. And it came late in another way, that is without the ever-lengthening commercial build-up and count-down that now reaches well back into Autumn. As M. V. Hughes records in her delightful *A London Child of the 1870s*: 'Nowadays it is difficult to realise that no Christmas preparations were made until the week before the day itself. All our excitement was packed into a short space.'

On the other hand, festivities once begun would continue unabated throughout the traditional Twelve Days, instead of petering out the day after Boxing Day and coming briefly back to life again at the turn of the year. That today's society has abandoned such protracted merrymaking is scarcely surprising (apart from the prohibitive cost); the prospect of twelve days' pre-packaged entertainment – probably in front of a television set – would daunt the most dedicated hedonist.

Our ancestors had one enormous advantage, however: they made their own entertainment, and most of that entertainment was music. The gramophone is no substitute; there is little to do with gramophone records once you have played them, except play them again (or not, as the case may be). With live, home-made music on the other hand, the variety is practically infinite. Piano solos, duets, carols, comic songs, rounds, recitations, however amateurishly performed will always be more exciting and involving than pre-recorded entertainments – particularly if the protagonists are your nearest and dearest.

As well as hanging up the mistletoe and holly, making the pudding, wrapping the presents and decorating the tree, Christmas meant sorting through the music cupboard for the well-tried favourites, and visits to the local dealer for this year's latest novelties. The standard of performance was not what counted, everything

The
Christmas Tree.
The
Bran Pie.
Lecturing Dolly.
Crackers.
Sliding.
Dressed for
a Charade.
Under
the Mistletoe.
Snowballing.
Fairy gifts from
Santa Claus.

was in the doing itself. (As G. K. Chesterton has said: 'If a thing is worth doing, it's worth doing badly'.) And if the performances were sometimes mediocre, the quality of the music performed was quite capable of competing with it – for *second* place. Enthusiasm was the key word for giving enjoyment, and at Christmas the Victorian family seemed positively larded with enthusiasm.

Neither was music confined indoors in Victorian life; Thomas Hardy and others have left vivid descriptions of the waits preparing their annual onslaughts of carols. Together with the armies of organ-grinders and other itinerant musicians who crowded the streets, Christmas shopping must have been an ear-splitting occupation – present-day supermarket 'seasonal' tape recordings would make Rudolph's red nose pale into insignificance by comparison. The streets were alive with the sound of music, as were the homes where, among the families of those who could afford one, the parlour piano was the focal point of social life. Musical evenings, a mainstay of Victorian intercourse, came into their own at Christmas and a whole new repertoire of domestic music came into existence.

All over England, something that was not quite Tin Pan Alley and not quite Grub Street but a heaven-sent mixture of the two, fostered hack composers and lyric-writers who throughout the year churned out polkas, schottisches and valses as if from a conveyor-belt. For the festive season, exactly the same style of music would be given appropriately dreamed-up titles like *Christmas Tree Dance* or *The Merry Waits:* identical in sound and sentiment to pieces which at other seasons might have become *Rustic Revelry* or *The Jolly Sailors*, for example. As always with popular music it was the packaging – the title and the cover – that clinched the deal

and sold the product. What lay between the covers was usually a secondary consideration.

The sheet-music industry was very big business indeed, equivalent to the recording industry today. Publishers, and sometimes composers, in the big league made fortunes for themselves and enjoyed the same kudos as companies dealing in the record charts now. If, accordingly, a neighbour's musical evening omitted the latest seasonal valse or galop, such a household would be considered very much behind the times.

Though it covered a very wide range, there was at Christmas of course a large quantity of sacred music. The nineteenth century saw an enormous revival in the old carols, which were now sung by all social classes instead of just the country-folk whom they had come from. There were new carols too, and 'sacred ballads' with a Christmas flavour. The latter were particularly popular. They would be sung on the Sunday after Christmas: such numbers as *The Holy City* and Gounod's *Nazareth* still lurk inside many a piano stool. For the very reason that carols and sacred music have been so well covered in anthologies, they have been omitted from this book, which concentrates on the abundance of secular music of the period.

Among the piano music and other instrumental pieces with seasonal titles, there flourished the Descriptive Fantasia. This extraordinary hybrid grew out of the earlier 'battle' pieces, which reach back as far as the Elizabethan age. Perhaps the most meretricious (and most popular) of all these was the late eighteenth-century *Battle of Prague* by Kotzwara, still popular in Victorian times (though we may be sure that the audience was never told of its composer found hanged in a brothel in the West

End of London). The Descriptive Fantasia tried to tell a story or paint a scene by a combination of music and verbal captions, and Christmas offered plenty of scope. Examples of this bizarre, unwieldy but disarming musical form appear throughout the book.

As for the songs, they vary from the sweetly predictable (the artless *Winter Evergreens* for example) to the really way-out (the amazing *Santy Claus is comin' 'fore de Morning'*). There are tear-jerkers too (*Now I've got No Daddy*), and the pantomime is well represented – this curious and unique dramatic form reached its peak of sumputousness at this period. Two more factors in A VICTORIAN CHRISTMAS SONG BOOK help recreate the flavour of that remarkable age. There are some musical games and puzzles that underline how seriously the earlier merry-makers took their fun. Secondly, great pains have been taken to preserve in the music the elegant engraving of the period; re-engraving the haunting and

evocative music of a hundred years ago would have robbed the original of much of its unique aura. Efforts have been made to restore the sometimes much-thumbed (and tear-stained) originals; it is to be hoped the result remains readily legible.

The vast bulk of the material reprinted here is strictly Victorian, though scholars may recognise that on occasion the music has strayed into a time that post-dated the late, great Queen. This is not cheating; eras commonly outlive their creators. The concept of the musical evening kept going well into the present century, until it was silenced by a combination of the gramophone and the First World War.

There are almost no pieces in A VICTORIAN CHRISTMAS SONG BOOK that will be found elsewhere: this is Christmas music with a difference. All the pieces here were in essence ephemeral – they made no claims to be considered as great art. They were written to amuse, and above all to entertain. From all ages in the long history of music, the great masterpieces survive; virtually all the opuscules in this book sank without a trace. Yet in its quaintness, its unpretentious charm and its ability to evoke a genteel age that is long past and unlikely ever to return, such music is probably unique. Accompanied at the piano by a large glass of port, it is something to be performed by *you*, and your friends. Especially at Christmas.

A CHRISTMAS HOLIDAY

Oscar Nielsen

This, a typical piece of its time, comes from a magazine *The Musical Budget* (1899). As so often happens with popular composers of the period, it is virtually impossible to discover details of their lives – partly because so many were amateurs who submitted such pieces to publishers and to magazines, and partly because so many composers used a multitude of pseudonyms.

A Christmas Holiday paints a naive but charming picture of the children's release and return from boarding-school. A journey of only thirty miles would have seemed like the other side of the world to a small child, with awe-inspiring trains belching steam and smoke, and the station-master giving imperious directions, in top hat, frock coat and side-whiskers.

Christmas itself was no less exciting. In the town square or on the village green, the Salvation Army band would have played, as it still does today. It might have played *Good King Wenceslas* which had been written only thirty years before and was becoming popular. Not well-known enough, however, for Nielsen to have got the tune exactly right.

tr
pp
Andante moderato.
"The dawn of Christmas."
mp
Very slow.
pp
poco rit.
ppp
pppp
"Christmas. The Carol Singers."
Maestoso. mp
mf
mp
cres.
molto rall.
"The Christmas party."
f Presto.
ff
sempre ff
Fine.

WHAT SHALL WE SING AT CHRISTMAS?

Words by Geo. Morriss · Music by R. Graham Harvey

This song, with its helpful suggestions, was already popular before it was reprinted in *The Musical Budget. Home, Sweet Home* and *Auld Lang Syne* are still sung at Christmas time, although *We Won't Go Home Till Morning* (from the French *Marlbrouk s'en va t'en guerre*) is now more familiar as *For He's a jolly good Fellow.* The words of the second verse, and the appearance of *Rule, Britannia*, are a reminder that the true Victorian was a patriot through and through. And in those days it was appropriate to sing about the home, absent friends, revelry and patriotism but not, apparently, about Jesus.

log is burn-ing bright; When wayward thoughts go wan-der-ing To those far from our sight? We'll sing the song they're
fire is bright and clear; Whilst 'neath the hol-ly-leaves we sit With those we love so dear? 'Tis well to think of
hearth is still a-light? For fa-ther says it is the rule—No one's ex-cused to-night! And when it comes his
log in em-bers gray De-clares the hour has come too soon That takes the guests a-way? Our hands will clasp in
cres.
dim. p
sure to sing, The song that brings to mind The fa-ces and the dear old spot The ex-iles left be-hind:
those who guard Our isles in peace or fight, To know that we are Eng-lish-men, And fear no des-pot's might:
wel-come turn He an-swers to the call, And, smil-ing, sings that jo-vial song Well known to one and all:
friend-ly grasp, And ga-ther'd in a ring, We'll show, in spite of Fa-ther Time, There's yet one song to sing:
cres.
CHORUS after 1st Verse. "Home, sweet Home!" (May be sung as a Solo in the absence of a Chorus.)
p Con espress.
rall.
D.C. for Symph.
'Mid plea-sures and pal-a-ces Tho' we............ may roam, There's no place like home, There's no place like home.
CHORUS after 2nd Verse. "Rule, Britannia!"
f
rall.
D.C. for Symph.
Rule, Bri-tan-nia! Bri-tan-nia rules the waves; Bri-tons nev-er, nev-er, nev-er shall be slaves!
CHORUS after 3rd Verse. "We won't go home till morning."
mf Giocoso.
cres.
D.C. for Symph.
We won't go home till morning, We won't go home till morn-ing, We won't go home till morn-ing, Till daylight does ap-pear.
V.S.

CHORUS after 4th Verse. "Auld Lang Syne."
f
Should old ac-quain-tance be for-got, And nev-er brought to mind, Should old ac-quain-tance be for-got, And
auld lang syne? For auld lang syne, my dears, For auld lang syne; We'll take a cup of
kind ness yet, For auld lang syne. *mp*
ff
FINE.

Sir Henry Bishop (1786–1855) will always be remembered for the popular ballad *Home, Sweet Home. The Mistletoe Bough*, a setting of Thomas Haynes Bayley's poem, is allegedly based on a true story and had already been used by the poet Samuel Rogers, in his *Italy*.

During the wedding feast of the young and beautiful Ginevra to a handsome nobleman, it was suddenly noticed that the bride was missing (Bishop's song suggests the guests were playing hide-and-seek). Neither the heartbroken husband, killed in battle a few weeks later, nor the demented father ever saw Ginevra again. Many years later a huge and ancient carved chest was found in one of the castle's forgotten galleries. It fell apart almost at a touch; in it lay a skeleton clad in a decaying bridal gown and wearing a wedding ring, jewels and a seal inscribed *Ginevra*.

A few years ago, after the author had revived the song for a television programme, a viewer wrote from Bristol to say that in the vaults of a solicitor's office there, are still to be found the remains of an old oak chest bearing the inscription *This is the Original Chest of the Song* THE MISTLETOE BOUGH.

In performing this piece, singer and accompanist must be alert to return to the appropriate places for verses 2 and 4, since no indication is given in the music.

f
p
1. The mis - tle - toe hung in the cas - tle hall, The hol - ly branch shone on the old oak wall; And the
2. "I'm wea - ry of danc - ing now," she cried, "Here tar - ry a moment, I'll hide, I'll hide! And
Ba - ron's re - tain - ers were blithe and gay, And keep - ing their Christ - mas hol - i - day. The
Lo - vell, be sure thou'rt the first to trace The clue to my se - cret lurk - ing place." A
mf
Ba - ron be - held with a fa - ther's pride His beau - ti - ful child, young Lo - vell's bride; While
way she ran, And her friends be - gan Each tow - er to search and each nook to scan; And
she with her bright eyes seem'd to be The star of the good - ly com - pa - ny,
young Lo - vell cried,— "Oh, where dost thou hide? I'm lone-some with - out thee, my own dear bride."

Oh, the mis-tle-toe bough, . . Oh, the mis-tle-toe bough. . . .
3. They sought her that night And they sought her next day, And they sought her in vain When a week pass'd a way; In the high-est, the low-est, the lone-li-est spot, Young Lo-vell sought wild-ly but
4. At length an oak chest That had long laid hid, Was found in the cas-tle— They rais'd the lid— And a skel-e-ton form lay mould-'ring there, In the bri-dal wreath of the
f
p

found her not. And years flew by, and their grief at last Was told as a sor - row - ful
la - dy fair! Oh, sad was her fate! in spor - tive jest She hid from her lord in the
tale long past; And when Lo - vell ap - pear'd the chil - dren cried, "See, the old man weeps for his
old oak chest; It clos'd with a spring, and her bri - dal bloom Lay with - 'ring there in a
fai - ry bride."
liv - ing tomb.
Oh! the mis - tle - toe bough, ...
Oh! the mis - tle - toe bough........
pp
pp

SONG OF THE ROBIN REDBREAST

Words by M. Bowcott · Music by Maria Bowcott

Maria Bowcott wrote both the words and music for this song; it seems to have been a convention to write the author's name in a different style to that of the composer, *cf.* Gatty's *Christmas Boxes.*

The cover (which follows this piece), typical of the best of its time, is particularly interesting. The artist was Thomas Packer, one of the leading lights in a somewhat specialised field, and who had a large palette of apprentices learning their craft in his studio. A close inspection of the cover reveals his subtle use of landscape and sky colouring, which earned him the sobriquet 'Graduated tint Packer'.

I am a lit - tle win - ter bird, And I have come out to - day,...... To
p
wish you all joy at this festive time Then open your window I pray.... For I
mf
Cres.
f
tap, tap, tap And I tap, tap, tap, Then I tap, tap, tap a - - gain.... I'll
mf
Cres.
mf
dim e rall.
sing you a carol of Christmas tide, If you'll come to the window pane....
sf
colla voce.

mf
mf
My redbreast's well known to young and old. For many a friend have I...... So I
p
Cres.
give a call here and I give a call there, And then to another I fly..... Where I
mf
Cres.
f
tap, tap, tap, And I tap, tap, tap, Then I tap, tap, tap, a - - gain... And
mf
Cres.
mf

dim e rall
sing them a carol of Christmas tide, When they come to the window pane....
sf
colla voce.
mf
mf
Molto espressivo e piu lento.
The beautiful snow is fall-ing fast, And win-t'ry winds are cold.... So I'll
p
bid you a-dieu with a hearty good wish. For blessings on young and on old.... Till I
mf
Cres.
f

tap, tap, tap, and I tap, tap, tap, Then I tap, tap, tap a-
mf
Cres.
gain.... Then I'll sing you a ca-rol of Christmas tide, If you'll
mf
sf
dim e rall.
come to the win--dow pane..........
colla voce.
mf
mf

Song of the
Robin Redbreast
WRITTEN & COM
BY
M. BOW
L.M.

WINTER EVERGREENS

Words by J. E. Carpenter · Music by Stephen Glover

Stephen Glover (1812–70) was one of the more prolific writers of best-sellers in his day, with about 1500 songs and piano pieces to his name. The family tenor with operatic aspirations would revel in the sheer floribundance of this melody, while the rich-sounding accompaniment never overtaxes the modest accomplishments of the gentle amateur.

The ro - - ses long have past their prime, The fruits no more are
p sempre stac.
seen, So let us chime a Christmas rhyme To hail - to hail the Ever-
p
green Though bright may be the summer wreath, To mourn it were but
f
p
folly, While friends delight to meet beneath The Mistletoe - the Mistletoe and
rall.
Cres.
rall.

dim.
a tempo.
Holly! Then circle round the ruddy blaze, And let but mirth be
sf
p a tempo.
seen, We still can raise, a song of praise To hail _ to hail the Ever_
Cres.
Cres.
f
Cres.
f
green! ..... To hail _ to hail the ever _ _ green! To hail _ to hail the ever_
f
p
Cres.
f
p
sf
green!
f Ped:
Ped:
sf
marcato.
ff

What though we rove the woods no more, Should we not still be
p sempre stac.
gay, When win_ _ter hoar, has leaves in store That never_that never fade a_
p
way? Some love to sing the joys of spring, With them why need we
f
p
quarrel, While jo_vial Christmas deigns to bring The Ivy_the Ivy and the
ral
Cres.
rall.

dim. a tempo.
Laurel? Then let us all each o_ther aid, Where friendship's wreath is
sf
p a tempo.
seen, 'Tis ne_ver made, of flow'rs that fade, But of the E_ver_
Cres.
Cres.
green! 'Tis never made of flowers that fade, But of_ but of the E_ver_
Cres.
f
f p Cres. f p sf
green!
Ped: Ped: sf marcato.
f ff

IT WAS MY FATHER'S CUSTOM

Words by James Stonehouse · Music by Frederick Shrival

The next song conjures up a picture of a typically Victorian Christmas. It is redolent of freshly-made punch and hearty laughter, so familiar from traditional Christmas cards. Other topical verses may suggest themselves as it is sung through – an ideal opportunity for the nimble rhymer to add a few impromptu lines of his own. (And for a nimble left hand, with a catchy bass in the second line of the song.)

1. Come hi-ther, bring the hol-ly bush, To de-cor-ate the wall, With no-ble bough of mis-tle-toe To hang a-mid the
2. Bring here the mas-sy yule log, The fire pile well up, For we must draw a-round it To drink the was-sail
3. Now see the guests as-sem-ble, With each a smil-ing face, They bend their heads in si-lence, To ask a ho-ly
4. Now clear a-way the ta-bles, And set a-side each chair, And let the mer-ry mu-sic For jo-cund dance pre-
hall; Spread wide the snow-y ta-ble cloth Up-on the shin-ing board, And bring the best of ev-'ry-thing the lar-der can af-
cup; The harm-less joke we'll pass a-bout, With spi-rits gay and light, Our laugh-ter too shall ring a-round, And e-cho here to-
grace; Now hark how plates are rat-tling, The guests en-joy the cheer, And see the vi-ands great and small, All swift-ly dis-ap-
pare; We'll play the games, the Christmas games, Blind man and hunt the shoe, And kiss the las-ses round and round, Beneath the mis-tle-
-ford; Ar-range a seat for ev-'ry guest, Let here the glass-es shine, It was my fa-ther's cus-tom, And so it shall be
-night; The old their gos-sip shall en-joy, The youth in mirth com-bine, These were my fa-ther's cus-toms, And so they shall be
-pear; Be gay, my friends, be mer-ry now, To feast let none de-cline, These were my fa-ther's cus-toms, And so they shall be
-toe; For Christmas joys come once a year, To hon-our them com-bine, It was my fa-ther's cus-tom, And so it shall be
mine, It was my fa-ther's cus-tom, And so it shall be mine.
mine, These were my fa-ther's cus-toms, And so they shall be mine.
mine, These were my fa-ther's cus-toms, And so they shall be mine.
mine, It was my fa-ther's cus-tom, And so it shall be mine.

GLAD TIDINGS

William Smallwood

Smallwood's Pianoforte Tutor! For nearly a century, how many thousands of pianists have been introduced to the delights and frustrations of learning through the medium of that venerable publication. William Smallwood (1831–97) passed virtually the whole of his working life as organist and choirmaster of Kendal Parish Church, in the heart of the English Lake District, and who can blame him for remaining there?

Apart from his indispensable *vade mecum* he composed hundreds of piano pieces and songs, establishing a substantial musical reputation and, very probably, an excellent income. *Glad Tidings*, an unpretentious and charming little piano piece (the composer calls it a 'sketch') was especially composed for the December 1895 edition of *Musical Answers*, a rare and interesting periodical aimed at the respectable amateur. The piece is shrewdly written – easy to play and, as a footnote says, suitable for organ or harmonium (at Christmas or at any other time, for that matter).

Oh bells that peal!
Oh bells that chime!
With music soft and clear,
Ring in a merry Christmas time
A bright and glad New Year
Andante (M.M. ♪=92).
p
cres.
mf
f

p
cres.
p
cres.
dim.
p
cres.
mf
f
mf
pp
rall.
Adagio.
cres.
dim.

NOW I'VE GOT NO DADDY

Words & Music by T. W. Connor

Our ancestors had a particular penchant for sentimental songs which could bring a tear to the eye. Even the humblest homes had their music making: in Charles Dickens's *A Christmas Carol* Tiny Tim helped to celebrate Christmas at the Cratchits by singing a song about a lost child travelling in the snow. Tim, adds the author, 'had a plaintive little voice, and sang it very well indeed'.

Now I've got no Daddy dates from 1907 and ends happily, if too late for the discerning pessimist. To avoid confusion, in the last line of the chorus after verse 3 the words might be changed to 'Although I've got no Daddy, He still has come to me', or some such.

The snow was fall - ing Christ - mas Eve! The shops a blaze with light And
The sis - ter wiped a - way the tears That would come to her eyes, And
The rich child told his Dad - dy what The lit - tle waif had said, And
p
crowds of chil - dren gaz - ing at The Christ - mas toys so bright One
told him of the San - ta - Claus Who lives be - yond the skies, And
that night dear old San - ta - Claus Stood by the slum child's bed, And
lit - tle shoe - less lad - die By his poor pale sis - ter led Turned
thinks of all the chil - dren, Be they rich or be they poor, Then
when he woke on Christ - mas morn The pre - cious toys were there, For
to a rich man's child near by And in - no - cent - ly said.
with a kiss she bade him not To mur - mur an - y more.
He who feeds the ro - bins, heard That lit - tle or - phan's prayer.
V.S.

CHORUS. 1st time p 2nd f
"San - ta - Claus" is com - ing! With his load of toys All so bright and
pret - ty For lit - tle girls and boys Once he used to bring some
For my Christ-mas tree But now I've got no Dad - dy He nev - er comes to me!" me!"
1.
2.
D.C.

THE BROKEN SLATE

Words by Edgar Bateman · Music by J. Airlie Dix

Another sentimental song, but with a pious touch so it might be performed with a clear conscience even when Christmas fell on a Sunday. The words take an unsettling turn in the second verse. The poor child certainly wanted a present, but being whisked up to Heaven seems a dubiously acceptable gift.

The composer, J. Airlie Dix, made his fame and probably his fortune with the once immensely popular ballad *Trumpeter, what are you sounding now?* which is still to be heard in occasional nostalgic radio and concert programmes.

Andante moderato.
PIANO.
p
rit.
p
1. It was Christ - mas Eve, and the night was chill, For the frost was in the air, And a
2. Then a shin - ing star in the win - try sky Of the child's re-quest took heed, And it
p
lit - tle boy sat on his lone - ly bed In a gar - ret so bleak and bare; A
lit up the words on the bro - ken slate So that heav - en - ly eyes might read. And the
poco accel.
bro - ken slate in his fin - gers cold— He wrote in the gath - 'ring gloom A
gifts the An - gels brought that night, From the Mas - ter Him - self sent down, Were
poco accel.
mes - sage to Fa - ther Christ - mas who Had nev - er been to that room. In the
free - dom from hun - ger, cold and pain, And a ti - ny gold en crown. When the

poco rit.
Refrain.
emp - ty grate, as the clock struck eight, He placed these words on the bro - ken slate:
sun rose fair in its splen - dour there It bath'd with glo - ry this an - swer'd pray'r,
"O Fa - ther Christ - mas,
poco rit.
if you come to this poor place to - night,.................. You are car - ry - ing joys to
poco rit.
a tempo.
hap - pi - er boys, And come for once you might................. I have no stock - ing that
I can hang, The chim - ney small may be,..................... But if you care a
accel.
rall.
pre-sent to spare...... Fa - ther, think of me!............... Please, just this once, of me!"............
rall.
D.C.

ONE TOUCH OF NATURE MAKES THE WHOLE WORLD KIN

Words & Music by Felix McGlennon

Only the second verse really justifies the inclusion of this irresistible song in a Christmas anthology. Its extraordinary popularity owed as much to its singer as to its intrinsic merits: Marie Loftus, one of the most celebrated of all music hall artistes, was born in 1857, and after a long and distinguished career (which included many world-wide appearances) died in 1940 at the age of eighty-three. She was often billed as the Hibernian Hebe although she came from Glasgow, not Ireland. Among the songs she made famous were *Sister Mary walked like that*, and this one: strong stuff – particularly the final stanza with its horrible warning.

Andante espressivo.
PIANO.
mf
FINE.
1. 'Tis night: the scene—a blood-stained bat - tle - field;.......... A truce till morn-ing seek the dead - ly foes,............ The
2. 'Tis Christ-mas eve—the joy - ous bells ring out,............ They seem to say, "Good will and Peace to all."............ The
3. Be - fore the judge de - fi - ant - ly she stands,......... Poor out - cast, drift-ing on the sea of life;............ The
p
ri - val armies fought, but none would yield,.................. The wea - ry sol-diers crave a brief re - pose.............. Ah!
vil-lage sleeps, nor heeds the royst'rer's shout,................ And silence reigns there in the rich man's hall............... But
drink fiend holds her, as in i - ron bands,................ Too help-less she to struggle in the strife;............. But
many a gal - lant heart in death is stilled,......... And many a com - rade mourns a com-rade dear;............ With
see! a burg - lar plies his law - less trade,......... With muf-fled feet and eag - er watch-ful eyes,............ On
slow-ly, sure - ly drift - ing, sink-ing down,.......... And yet she once was some poor mo-ther's pride,............ Now
dreams of glo - ry ev - 'ry sol - dier's thrilled,............ Though death is nigh, no thought have they of fear. ....
plun-der bent, of cap - ture not a - fraid, ... He grim - ly whispers, "He who'd cross me dies."...........
reck-less there, nor heeds the judg - e's frown, ... Poor Mag - da-len!—far bet - ter had she died. ....
V.S.

Chorus.
Crouch-ing round the camp - fires, in the rud - dy glow, While the watchful sen - tries pace there to and fro,
Creep -ing there, so steal - thy, in the si - lent gloom, Search-ing for his plun - der, all a - round the room,
" I was once so pure, sir, in - no - cent and young, Till the temp-ter came, sir, with his ly - ing tongue,
Wait-ing for the morn - ing, then to face the foe, Ea - ger all a he - ro's name to win. ....
" I'll stop not at mur - der, though death be my doom ! " Des-p'rate is his heart and steep'd in sin. ....
What cared he tho' my heart was with an-guish wrung, Tho' I drift - ed in the path of sin. ....
" We've been good old chums, Jack, naught could part us two ; If my time has come, Jack, and if spared are you,
Hark ! a ti - ny voice there, " Take me on your knee, Are you San - ta Claus, please ? No toys can I see ! "
In the vil - lage church I used to kneel in pray'r ; Would you know the name of him who laid the snare ?
Tell the lit - tle girl I love, I was ev - er true." One touch of na - ture makes the whole world kin.
" Good-night, lit - tle dar - ling one ! kiss me, pray for me ! " One touch of na - ture makes the whole world kin.
You were my be - tray - er, sir ! judge me, if you dare ! " One touch of na - ture makes the whole world kin.
p
D.C.

MOTHER AND THE DEAR OLD DAD

Words & Music by Charles Wilmot & Will Godwin

Subtitled 'A song of Home', this piece was tailor-made for the music hall, as the cue for 'Bells' and the 'Till ready' sign also indicate. And so it was, with the famous Will Godwin co-authoring the words and music.

During the 'till ready' introduction, the singer's duty would be to remind his audience (not that they would need much prompting) to charge their glasses and join in the toast at the end of each verse.

1. 'Twas
2. My
3. I
Bells.
Till ready.
PIANO.
Christ-mas Eve, and the Eng-lish post Had just ar-rived at the West................ There was
thoughts that night slow-ly wan-dered back To all the dear ones once more,............... They were
dream the winds bring me safe-ly home, And all is cheer-ful a-gain................ There are
ma-ny a sigh, and ma-ny a tear That night be-fore going to rest......................
all in peace, the fire shone bright Red gleams on the snow through the door......................
two fond hearts so pleased to know Their prayers have not been in vain......................
"Here's to the girl I love!" said one. "Here's to us all!" said an-oth-er.
One pret-ty girl a-lone I saw Bu-sy with i-vy and hol-ly,
"Home, home, sweet home!" the hap-py throng Stand there in har-mon-y sing-ing,
"Here's to the grand old la-dy we love— What a grand old name is mo-ther!
Hang-ing it round my face on the wall, 'Twas the girl I love, sweet Pol-ly!
Kiss-ing wher-e'er the mis-tle-toe hangs, As the Christ-mas bells are ring-ing.
Ped.

CHORUS. 2nd time ff.
"I can see all the fam - i - ly Sit - ting round the fire so bright................
I can see the girl I love Hang - ing up the mis - tle - toe up - on the walls to - night. I can
hear their voi - ces ring - ing, As they did when I was a lad; .... I can
see two grey heads nest - tl - ing to - geth - er— Mo - ther and the dear old dad."
1st.
2nd.
dad."
FINE.
D.C.

A browse through any pile of Victorian music will uncover, sooner rather than later, a 'characteristic piece' by Ezra Read. His biographical details are elusive, but his vast output of hundreds of pieces, with fanciful titles and flamboyant covers, depicted battles, shipwrecks, disasters and homely little scenes such as this one. As well as being eminently danceable, these 'programme' pieces as they are technically known, have distinguished precedents. Descriptive fantasias were much in demand for the virginals in the time of Queen Elizabeth I.

CHRISTMAS MORN.
mf
rall.
THE WAITS. "Christians, awake."
mp Religioso.
rall.
"Old Folks at Home."
mf Moderato.
rall. e dim.
THE GREETING.
mf Allegro.
HAPPY RE-UNION.
f
f

A Merry Gathering.
f
rall.
A Happy Family.
"When there's love at home."
There is beau - ty all a - round
When there's love at home;
There is joy in ev - 'ry sound,
When there's love at home;
Peace and plen - ty here a - bide,
Smil - ing sweet on ev - 'ry side,
Time doth soft - ly, sweet - ly glide,
When there's love at home. . . .
rall.
"Sir Roger de Coverley."
f Allegro.
f
Fine.

CHRISTMAS 1874

Words by R. A. Gatty · Music by Alfred Scott Gatty

The next two songs come from a charming collection *Little Songs for Little Voices*, and though written for children, manage to avoid excess sentimentality.

The noble and well-connected Alfred Scott Gatty K.C.V.O. and Garter King-of-Arms (1847–1918) was the son of a clergyman, and was not merely the composer of songs and operettas but also author of several childrens' books. What was the significance of 1874 for the composer? It might have been the publisher's idea of a topical theme or – the only event of that year which had any remote connection with Christmas – it might have been the financial collapse of Turkey.

2.

The happy sounds of Christmas-tide are heard again by all;
Old customs of the country side, with carols in the hall.
Bright hours! that pass like flowers away before the hearth is cold;
So swiftly each new Christmas Day is gathered with the old!
CHORUS.—Then heigho! for the winter snow, &c.

CHRISTMAS BOXES

Words & Music by Alfred Scott Gatty

In the second of these songs by Gatty, there is a reference to *snap-dragon*. This was a popular Victorian parlour game played at the end of dinner. Miss Sheila Jessop, from Borth in North Wales, has vivid recollections:

'Just after the First World War my sister, mother and I were asked to a fireworks party each year at a country house near Aberystwyth. After a good tea we children stood in the windows of the drawing-room behind the curtains and watched a wonderful display of fireworks. After this we were taken down to the cellar with wide slate floors and into a large room with a big, scrubbed pine table down the middle, and benches on either side – I should think it used to be the tenants' hall. When we were all seated, Sir Lewes and Ceredig, the butler, would come in with the *snapdragons*. These were *very* large dishes piled high with raisins on which some brandy or other spirits had been poured and then set alight. These were put at intervals down the centre of the table and we grabbed raisins and ate them. It was great fun, and they tasted very good.'

2. Come, give a cheer for one who brings
   Kind presents to us all ;
 He brings to parents back from school
   Their children, great and small.
     A holly crown, &c.

3. Mince pies, plum puddings, pleasant gifts
   He brings the children, too ;
 Snap-dragon, flaming in the dish,
   Which makes them look so blue.
     A holly crown, &c

4. Sweet mem'ries of the past he brings,
   As age recalls the day
 When life was full of youth and hope,
   And everything was gay.
     A holly crown, &c.

5. And still more precious gifts he brings,
   Whenever Christmas comes ;
 Peace and goodwill, goodwill and peace
   To Christian hearts and homes.
     A holly crown, &c

A CHRISTMAS PARTY

Ezra Read

Ezra Read's endless 'Descriptive Fantasias' may now seem musically insubstantial but they were popular enough in his time, to judge by the number of amateur pianists who bought them. This one, perhaps with the pianist sporting bell bracelets (price 2/2d per pair, post free) must have been a real barnstormer. Compare Read's evocation of a Christmas party with that of the Fezziwigs in Dickens's *A Christmas Carol*, and notice the reference to *The Mistletoe Bough* (page 19).

Bells.
Piano.
pp staccato.
Relatives and Friends arrive.
Moderato.
f
rall:
The Waits.
Religioso.
mf

Under the Mistletoe.
Moderato.
mp
rall:
Playing at Forfeits.
Moderato.
mp

mf
rall:
mp
Playfully. Round the Xmas tree.

mf
Off to the Frozen Lake.
f
ten:
cresc:
ten:
rall:
trem:
Allegro. On the Ice.
Merry Skaters
f

The return home by Moonlight.
f
cresc:
ff

The Dance · Sir Roger de Coverly.
Allegro.
Breaking up of Dance.
trem. ff
Round the Fire.
Moderato.
mf
Telling Fairy Tales.
Tempo di Valse.
mp

1.
2.
Bed-time.
8
f
8
ff
Good-
night good-night good-night.
1
ff
Fine.

CHRISTMAS BELLS

Words by Steve Leggett · Music by Will Godwin

Another of Will Godwin's music hall numbers, *Christmas Bells* was popularised by the comedian Leo Dryden. The music seems at first glance to be in waltz time, but this is a sentimental, nostalgic number. When the beer and brandy were beginning to take their euphoric toll, then the soloist and his audience (joining in just one more chorus) might relish its unhurried, wallowing tempo.

Moderato.
Bells.
mf
Tempo di Valse.
f
1. All hail to old Fa _ ther Christmas a gain! He on _ ly comes once a _
2. The mis _ tle _ toe sweet is the emblem of love, Wher _ e'er an Eng _ lish _ man
3. In ev' _ ry home there's a welcome for all! And little ones nev _ er will
p
year; . . . . With a song or a tale or a cup of good ale, 'Tis the
roams. . . . . Be it mo _ ther or Miss, be _ neath it they kiss, And it
tire, ... Of the tales that are told by dear grandpa so old, As they

same for the poor as the Peer! . . . . Good for _ tune at _
hangs there in all Eng _ lish homes! . . . . In pal _ ace or
ga _ ther a round by the fire! . . . . A _ way burns the
_ tend, Each mer _ ry man's friend; Though beau _ ty and youth may de _
cot The place mat _ ters not Wher _ ev _ er our flag's un _
log, A _ round goes the grog! The old and the young ones all
_ cay! . . . . For _ get _ ting old wrongs, with ca _ rols and
_ furled . . . . For _ get and for _ give! where e'er we may
sing, ... And peace and good will on earth it is
songs They drive the old year a _ way! . . . . The
live! It's Christmas all over the world! . . . . The
still As joyously all the bells ring! . . . . The

CHORUS.
Christmas bells are chiming..... In - vi - ting all to pray!......
Fa - thers, mo - thers sis-ters and brothers Are hap-py on Christmas day!..... For
- getting old wrongs, with carols and songs, The old and the young are gay!..... And welcome the
new year once a - gain, And drive the old year a - way The - way
1.
2.
D.C.

MISS HOOLIGAN'S CHRISTMAS CAKE

Anon

This delightful number was sung by Harry Melville, 'The Irish Daisy'. Described as a Capital Irish Convivial Song, *Miss Hooligan's Christmas Cake* has all the musical ingredients of a traditional jig, while the plums, prunes and cherries of the song (though not the glue) go into every good Christmas cake. A lively and spirited piece, it well repays a careful run-through before the party, and the company will all want to join in the rousing chorus.

Animato.
1. As I sat at my win_dy last evenin', The
2. Miss Mul_li_gan want_ed to taste it, But
3. Mrs Hoo_li_gan proud as a peacock, Kep'
4. Ma_ _lo_ney was took with the col_ic, Mc_
let_ter man brought unto me,... A lit_tle giltedg'd in_vi_ta_tion, Sayin' Gil
real_ly there was_n't no use,... They work'd at it o_ver an hour, And they
smil_in' and blink_in' a_way,... 'Till she fell o_ver Flan_i_gan's bro_gans And
_Nul_ty complain'd of his head,.. Mc_Fad_den laid down on the so_fy And
_hoo_ly come o_ _ver to tea,..... Sure I knew that the Hoo_li_gans'
couldn't get none of it loose,.... 'Till Hoo_li_ _gan wint for the
spill'd a whole brew_in' of tay,..... "Oh, Gil_hoo_ly" she cried "you're not
swore that he wish'd he was dead.... Miss Da_ _ly fell down in hys_
sent it, So I wint just for old friend_ship's sake,..... And the
hat_chet, And Kil_ _ly came in with a saw,..... That
'a_ _tin'," Try a lit_ _tle bit more for my sake...... "No,
_ter_ics And there she did wrig_gle and shake..... While

first thing they gave me to tackle, Was a slice of Miss Hoo_li_gan's cake . . . .
cake was e_nough by the powers, To par_a_lyze a_ny man's jaw . . . . .
thanks Misses Hoo_li_gan," sez I, "But I'd like the re_sate of that cake. . . . .
ev'_ry man swore he was poison'd Thro' 'a_ _tin' Miss Hoo_li_gan's cake". . . .
CHORUS.
There was plums and prunes and cherries, And citron and raisons and cinnamon too, There was
nut_megs cloves and berries, And the crust it was nail'd on with glue. There was
ca_ra_way seeds in a_bundance, Sure 'twould build up a fine stomachache, You would
kill a man twice af_ter 'ating a slice Of Miss Hoo_li_gan's Christmas cake. . . . .

SANTY CLAUS IS COMIN' 'FORE DE MORNIN'

Words by C. L. Mays · Music by M. P. Hunter

Dating from 1898, this must be among the most implausible Christmas songs ever written, and stretches credulity to its limits. While the picture of a poor negro slave bewailing the loss of Christmases past in captivity is bizarre enough, *Santy Claus* does reflect the great nineteenth-century popularity of blacked-up minstrels. This song evidently became popular enough to merit at least one pirate edition, a copy of which is in the author's possession.

High Life below Stairs.

Moderato.
PIANO.
mf
Ped.
f
p
1. I don't care much a - bout de sun - - shine, And
2. De mock - in'-bird sing - in' in de eve - - nin'— De
3. But some time I'm a - goin' to wan - - der
don't bo - ther much a - bout de rain,
sun am a - set - tin' in de West,
Back to de cot - ton fields a - gain.
I'm al - ways think - in' ob de south - ern clime And a
De work's all o - ber in de cot - ton field, An' de
I can't help brood - in' o - ber by - gone times, An' my
home I may nev - er see a - gain........................
dark - ies, dey hab a lit - tle rest........................
tears start a - fall - in' like de rain;........................
Try - in' migh - ty hard to keep from
Pic - ca - nin - nies run to meet their
Si - lent voi - ces make me bro - ken -
weep - - in',
mam - - mies,
- heart - - ed,
Long - in' for de Mis - sis - sip - pi shore,........................
Mer - ry voi - ces ring - in' on de air—........................
Set - tin' me a - weep - in' more and more,........................

Where de steam-boats used to go a-sweep - in' By my ca - bin door. ....
Pret - ty soon de moon be - gin a - shin - in', Di - nah meets me dere. ....
Find - in' all de dark - ies hab de - part - ed For dat gold - en shore. ....
CHORUS.
I do feel sor - ry dat I was set free, Mas - sa and mis - sus were so good to me. My
2nd time ff.
heart's just ach - in' and a - break - in' Their fa - ces just to see once more.
Pic - ca - nin - nies sing - in' roun' de fire so bright; Hang - in' up their stock - ings on Christ - mas night, 'Cause
San - ty Claus is com - in' 'fore de morn - in' To de cab - in on de Mis - sis - sip - pi shore. I shore. ....
1st.
2nd.
D.C.

UNDER THE MISTLETOE

Words & Music by A. J. Mills & Harry Castling

The popularity of the pantomime came to overshadow the music hall at Christmas. As a consequence there were only a few songs, like *Under the Mistletoe*, for those who remained faithful to the old traditions. The 'Till ready' formula (*cf. Mother and dear old Dad* page 49) allows for any stage business that the comic singer might use to help the song go with a swing. On this point it is important that the performer makes sure, before taking the platform, to equip himself with the customary saprophytic sprig, as directed in the last verse. This song is best sung accompanied – preferably by a large glass of port.

Voice.
Piano.
Allegro moderato.
ff
sf
p
ad lib.
mp
1. A grand and jol - ly old cus - tom you will find at Christ - mas time,............... In
ev - 'ry house you go, hangs the bunch of Mis - tle - toe................... You

2.

The sweet and spooney young couple, oh! they quite enjoy the fun.
They wander to and fro, underneath the Mistletoe;
And when the couple are man and wife the following Christmastide,
Before them all he'll boldly kiss the bride.
Another Christmas day comes round, and then the happy pair,
They're at the same old game, and now they're kissing a son and heir.
Under the Mistletoe, &c.

3.

Now there's the grumpy old batch'lor who's in diggings all alone,
The servant gives a grin as she brings the turkey in;
A feeling then overcomes him he has seldom felt before,
He sees the Mistletoe above the door.
He gives the girl a Christmas box, then steals a kiss with glee;
It's only once a year, of course he likes it and so does she.
Under the Mistletoe, &c.

4.

The sweet kiss under the Mistletoe will always be the thing,
It gives the modest miss excuses for a kiss;
You kiss her under the parlour stairs, her dignity she'll show,
She likes it underneath the Mistletoe.
A bunch of Mistletoe's the thing to bring you perfect bliss—
I always carry some myself (*produce Mistletoe*)—would anyone like a kiss?
Under the Mistletoe, &c.

CHORUS.

Un - der the Mis - tle - toe - o, Un - der the Mis - tle - toe, ...
mp (2nd f)
Young maids, old maids, dear - ly love to go............... Oh! did you ev - er,
ev - er hear a girl say "No"............... When you whis - per
1st.
D.S.
2nd.
"Come and kiss me Un - der the Mis - tle - toe"?............... - toe"?............
ff
D.C.

A CHRISTMAS PANTOMIME

Mel. B. Spurr

Pantomime came into its own as a Christmas institution towards the end of the nineteenth century. Till then it had had no specific ties with any particular season of the year. By the 1880s, from Drury Lane Theatre down to the meanest village-hall in Britain were peopled with Ugly Sisters, Dames, Fairy Queens, Principal Boys, and toothy but toothsome chorus girls.

It was also a great age for home theatricals. At Christmas there were charades, one-act plays, sketches and – inevitably – home pantos. An industry evolved to cater for such modest activities, producing scripts, costumes and even simple props.

The next item is something of a curiosity (and a misnomer). It is in fact a monologue, performed by the author/composer. A few careful rehearsals (and a well-groomed prompter) enable an imaginative performer to bring uniquely to life again this extraordinary souvenir of Christmas long ago.

It is an old custom of mine — and, doubtless, of yours as well — to pay a visit every year to the Pantomime. Many old fogies tell us that "Pantomimes are not what they used to be when *they* were young." (Somehow nothing ever *is* good enough for the old fogies!) But every year, as Christmas time comes round, the old feeling steals over us, and in the merry festive season of mince-pies and plum-pudding we feel irresistibly impelled to trudge through the slush and brave the elements to see some good old Nursery story turned inside out and upside-down, and to laugh again heartily at the merry capers of the Clown and Pantaloon.

Now, I want you to imagine, for a few moments, that we are waiting outside our favourite theatre — whichever that may be — for the doors to open. We will resolve *not* to mingle on this occasion, as we invariably do, with the swells in the stalls and boxes, but to view the humours of a pantomime from the altitude of the Gallery. And here we are outside, amongst the Gallery-ites, waiting. And how the Gallery-ites do squeeze and jostle, to be sure. Here's one old lady, who must weigh sixteen stone, if she weighs an ounce, has got somehow jammed against a door-post. "Oh, William," she says to her husband, "they're a-squeezin' me." To which her loving husband responds *"Shut up!"* Then we have, in various voices, "Now then, where are you shovin', can't you?" "Joe! *Joe!* Here's this feller a-diggin' his elber into my ribs." "Here, mum, if it don't make no difference to *you* — which it does a good deal to *me* — *would* you mind a-takin' of your sixteen stone weight orff of my favourite corn? — Thank you!" And now a noise is heard inside: a heavy bolt is shot back and — *Whoosh!* — the crowd rushes in, pell-mell. Up the stairs we go like wild-fire, and arrive at the top, quite out of breath. The boys exchange their usual greetings with each other, right across the theatre, and the people all round settle down steadily to their *meals,* which they have brought with them in baskets. The dear old ladies are drinking out of little flat bottles. *(Imitate drawing cork, refreshing, replacing cork, wiping mouth with back of hand, &c.)* Some are eating whelks — some winkles — *(shudder of disgust.)* The old lady — the professor of avoirdupois — has brought a cow-heel with her, which she is eating with evident relish, and then the musicians come in to the orchestra, and begin tuning up.

Suddenly the conductor taps on the desk before him, *(business)* the tuning ceases, and with a few crashing chords the band goes off into the Overture. *(Imitate, banging chords, wielding bâton, &c.)*

With a few more crashing chords the Overture comes to a conclusion, — "Ting!" goes on the prompter's bell, and up goes the curtain.

The Pantomime, we'll suppose, is called "Jack the Giant Killer, or Harlequin Old Mother Hubbard, Little Bo-Peep, Boy-Blue, and the King of the Cannibal Islands."

As the curtain ascends, we discover the usual number of demons, who are industriously hammering nothing whatever on a very large anvil. They sing the opening Chorus, and as their voices sound through huge masks the effect is somewhat quaint — muffled, so to speak. One of the demon's jaws has got loose, and vibrates spasmodically and spontaneously — *(Observe this in singing Chorus.)*

Opening Chorus of Demons.

Then the first demon says *(muffled voice for Demons.)*

"Attend, ye demons, let us shout and sing,
And cheer with three times three to greet our King.–Hurray!"

2nd Demon. (another voice) "Hurray!" *3rd Demon. (with waggling jaw)* "Hurray!" *(shut jaw to with hand.)*

Here the Demon King shoots up a trap. *(Chord on piano, as below, then trap business.)*

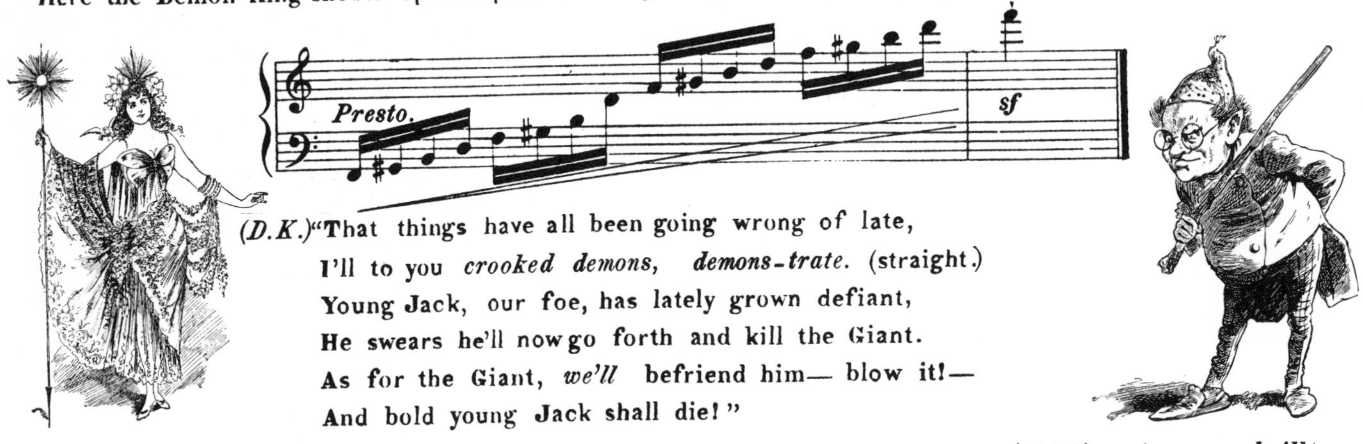

(D.K.) "That things have all been going wrong of late,
I'll to you *crooked demons, demons-trate.* (straight.)
Young Jack, our foe, has lately grown defiant,
He swears he'll now go forth and kill the Giant.
As for the Giant, *we'll* befriend him— blow it!—
And bold young Jack shall die!"

A little Fairy Queen about so high *(indicating 3 feet)* enters, and says, *(Child's voice, very shrill.)*

"Not if *I* know it!
I will defeat your plans, and save his life.
Now war's declared between us — to the knife."

The Fairy Queen's Song.

There you have the opening Scene in a few seconds. The scene now changes to Fairyland, where all the trees seem to grow fruit of tinsel and Dutch metal, and several *very* substantial-looking fairies come on, and begin flopping about the stage in all directions. *(Play Ballet Music on piano to the end of this description.)*

Ballet Music.

The little boy in the boxes says to his mamma: "Oh, mamma, look at the boo ful ladies." *(Mamma)* Yes, my dear, they're the pretty fairies that I've told you about." *(Boy.)* "Oh, is they? I thought they were too fat for fairies. *(pause.)* Can *I* be a fairy, ma, when I grow up?" *(Mamma.)* "Hush, don't be so absurd." And now the *prèmiere danseuse* comes on, and begins capering about, like a parched pea in a frying-pan. She finally subsides into the arms of two of those *very* substantial-looking fairies aforesaid, and the scene is closed in with red fire. *(Stop music.)*

V.S.

The scene now changes to the exterior of Jack's cottage. Jack's mother comes on. She is the comic old woman of Pantomime, and is, of course, played by a man— that being the rule in Pantomime, where things do get a bit mixed and topsy-turvy. The old woman is played by a man: the principal boy is played by a young girl— a more or less young girl. Jack's mother has come from the wash-tub, and she rubs off the suds on entering. *(Imitate.)* She thus delivers herself of her woes:

"It's hard to be a widder, poor and lone,
Reduced by poverty to skin and bone.
A widder, with an idle, graceless sonny,
Who, 'stead of working, spends my
hard-earned money.

What I do for that boy there's no one knows:
I wash his dinner, and I cook his clothes.
You wouldn't think that I was half so spry—
But, there! You never know what you can do,—
till you try!

This suggests the topical song— without which no Pantomime is genuine.

"I fancy I could if I tried."

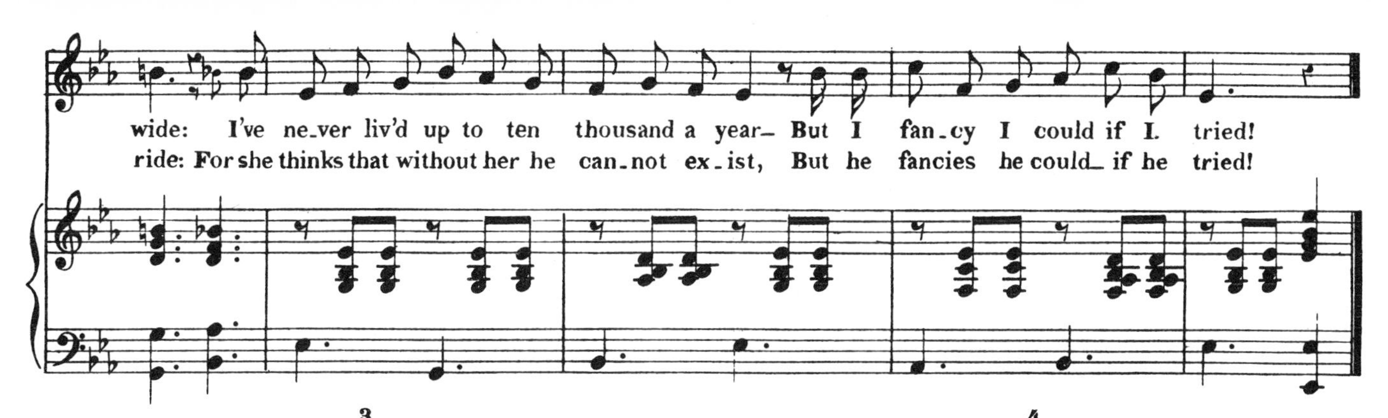

3

That the ladies have brains they're determined to show,
To their rights they are all wide-awake:
Some are starting to practise as doctors, you know,
And very nice doctors they make!
That some day they'll get into Parliament, too,
Is a fact that can not be denied:
I hope they'll talk members to death, if they do,
For I'm *certain* they could if they tried.

4

For the glory of adding M. P. to their name
It's astounding what candidates do:
They'll bribe, and they'll slander, and cheat and defame,
And think themselves justified, too.
A voter can always get paid for his vote,
If he's willing to pocket his pride:
I've never sold mine for a cheque or a note,
But I'm certain I could if I tried.

Jack's mother, at the conclusion of the song, goes off, and the stage is now filled with villagers for the Maypole Dance. Jack comes on.

The Maypole Dance.

Jack is, of course, in love with Margery Daw, the village beauty, and— equally of course,—the Giant Grumblegrim has his eye upon her. (Literally his eye, for he only has one.) Margery comes in, followed by Bo-peep, who is in search of her favourite sheep, which have been lured away by the giant, to satisfy his enormous appetite. Jack is to go and rescue these sheep, the reward of his success being Margery's hand. Jack says:-

"I'll find the sheep: but come! it's time to start.
Farewell, my *bitter-jam:* good-bye *sweet-tart*." *(Imitate embrace.)*

V.S.

The scene changes to the Giant's kitchen. *(Melo-dramatic Music.)* Giant is discovered, dozing. *(Snore.)*

He comes down to the footlights, and observes:-

"Fee fi, Fo fum! I smell the blood of an Englishman. *(huge sniff.)*
Be he alive or be he dead I'll grind his bones to make me bread."

Jack scuttles into the coal-cellar, with the remark:

"Perhaps for the present I'd best disappear:
A good *idea*: I think I'd best *hide-here*."

Margery now enters. The giant sees her, seizes her, is about to kill her and boil her down for supper afterwards, when suddenly Jack rushes out of the cellar with his drawn sword: at the same time Jack's mother comes in with a gingham umbrella, with which she hits the giant a tremendous whack on the head. A terrific combat now ensues. *(Chords on piano, lowest bass notes.)* The giant is down on his marrow-bones: Jack is just about to *slew* him *(glissando, in treble.)* when the Giant's guards, in big masks, come on, seize Jack and Margery, and convey them to the lowest dungeon of the castle-keep.

The stout old lady in the gallery is now intensely excited, and waves her cow-heel over her head. *(Business.)* She is only calmed down by a liberal application to the little flat-bottle. *(Imitate, as before.)*

Meanwhile, Jack and Margery are in durance vile in the lowest dungeon of the castle-keep, which gives an opportunity for Margery to observe, when Jack attempts to kiss her:-

"You mustn't kiss me here— you shan't have one, John:
What? In a dungeon, Jack? Now do *ha' done-John*."

Margery still being reluctant, Jack endeavours to coax her in a little song—

Kissing Song.

And now the Giant enters to kill the lovers. The club is raised to strike the fatal blow. You could almost hear a cart-wheel drop in the house. Then, suddenly, that little Fairy Queen comes in with a tin sword about so long *(measuring a foot and a half)* in her hand, with which she prods the Giant twice in the stomach, exclaiming:-

(Shrill voice.) "You bold, bad man: how *could* you be so cruel?
Take that *(thrust)* and that: *(ditto)* there! now he's got his gruel!"

The Giant, of course, falls, mortally wounded, and from all sides the fairies troop on, singing Jack and Margery's "Bridal Chorus."

Bridal Chorus.

Everything ends happily: everybody is married to every body else, but before the Finale is reached, the performers make their appeals to the audience, in the approved fashion. The Giant revives, comes forward, and says:-

"I've been a bad 'un: broken all the laws: So pray reward me with your kind applause."

Then the little Fairy Queen says:

"Without my aid, where would poor Jack have been? So don't forget the little Fairy Queen." *(curtsey.)*

Finally. Jack comes jauntily down and observes:

"Though Margery is mine, one thing I lack, So give a rousing cheer for young Friend Jack."

Then comes the Transformation Scene: lots of tinsel, lots of red, blue, yellow, green and purple fires. Fairies are wound up, and fairies are wound down again, and then we hear: *(Clown's speech spoken through Hurry Music.)*

Hurry Music.

(CLOWN.) "Hallo! Here we are again! How was you to-morrow? How are you going to be the day before yesterday? Oh, here's a nice sweet-stuff shop! Come along, Daddy. A merry Christmas and a happy New Year to everybody! *(broad grin à la Clown.)*

Finale.

LM

The Schottische was originally the Germanic idea of what a Scottish dance was like; the title 'Schottische' extends back at least as far as Beethoven. In the nineteenth century it was a popular dance, and is still familiar to Olde Tyme Dance enthusiasts. J. Stein's dance is typical of the unsophisticated occasional music of the time. It will have been given its title as most suitable to the time of its publication rather than for any connection it had with the season, or the theatre.

1st time.
2nd time.
mf
To Coda
TRIO.
mf

Dal 𝄋
CODA.
ff
FINE.

A WINTER RIDE

Theo. Bonheur

Musical Rides became a great rage in Victorian times. There was a *Spring Ride* and an *Autumn Ride*, a *Sleigh Ride* and a hundred others including this *Winter Ride*. It is obviously time to bring out the bell bracelets again (*cf. A Christmas Party*, page 59). The composer, Theo. Bonheur, was almost as prolific as Ezra Read, though his tunes are more memorable. His real name was Alfred Rawlings, which possibly explains the exotic pseudonym.

Tempo di Galop.
p
Cres:
mf
Cres:
f
f marcato.

p
Cres:
mf
Cres:
f

p
8va
8va
8va

f
p

Coda.
p
Cres:
Cres:
f
ff
fz

Musical Games were always in demand at the end of the year. *The Musical Home Journal* was happy to provide appropriate material. To paraphrase the onlie begetter of *The Kitchen Band*, Clement A. Harris: This is a grand game for gatherings of musical friends. It is here arranged for fourteen players – a pianist, conductor and twelve instrumentalists, though it can be played by fewer (or more, with two players to a part). A conductor *and* a pianist are essential.

The 'Grand symphonic poem for chorus and orchestra' will need a few minutes' rehearsal with each part separately. It is primarily a game and, like all good games, benefits from a little careful preparation. The archaic introductory text has only been updated where it may help performers assemble suitable instruments. In centrally-heated apartments today, grid-irons, pokers and zinc baths are now rare.

PIANO: or any keyboard instrument.
VIOLIN: real instrument, or strong, thin string tied to a table leg at one end. It may be plucked (tightening and slackening according to the pitch of the melody), or bowed by a resined string fixed to a length of bent cane. Some kind of resonator, such as a hollow box, would help swell the volume.
DOUBLE BASS: as for violin (*above*) but with much longer and thicker string. The traditional tea-chest-with-a-walking-stick-on-top-of-it principle gives the idea exactly. Electric cable plucks well.

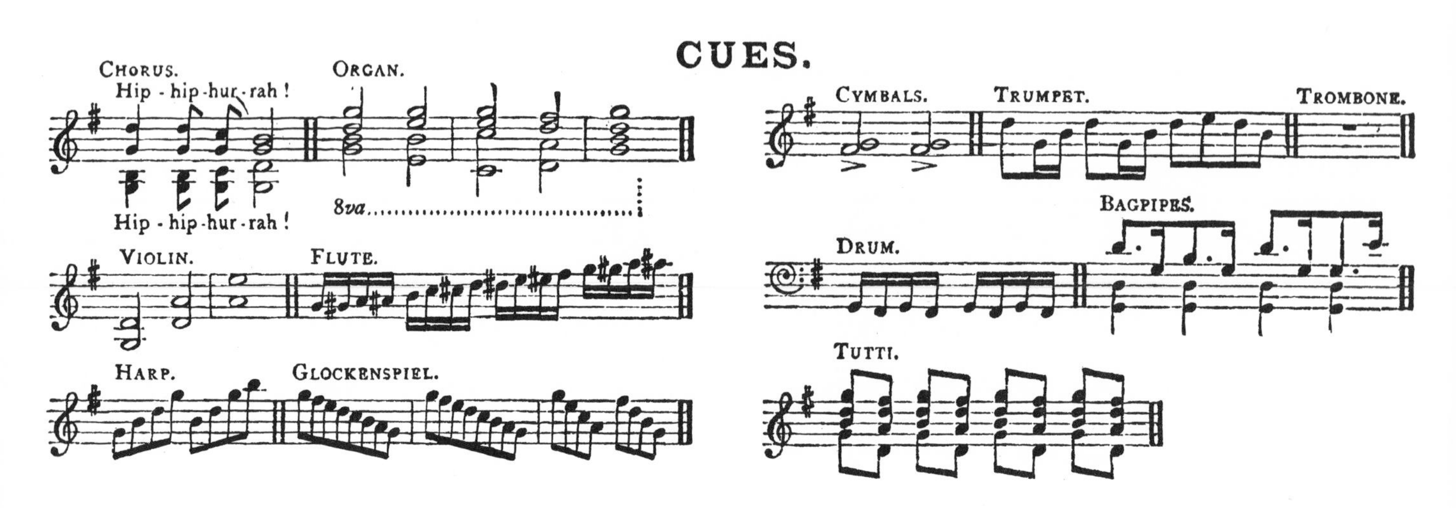

TROMBONE: a cycle pump with the handle held away from the mouth and drawn in and out, suggests the *appearance* of this instrument ludicrously well. It should be assigned to a gentleman guest, who must 'tootle' sonorously while playing it.
HARP: metal toast-rack or oven shelf played with a skewer or other thin metal rod.
ORGAN: a mouth organ, close-harmony chorus, or even controlled whistling.
FLUTE: penny whistle or some such; a 'Swanee' type whistle will do the chromatic scale required of it, most elegantly.
DRUM: a large, shallow metal bath, an upside-down metal waste paper basket or similar; tie a duster in a lump around a piece of stick as a beater. (If two drums – with something like adjacent pitches – can be improvised, the effect will be improved.
BAGPIPE: inflated balloon. The performer may let the air squawk out of the balloon to fit (and in time with) the bass drone, while crowing his melody in like fashion.
CYMBALS: two saucepan lids (without rims, if possible). They should be held a little loosely, and should approach each other gently from an angle.
TAMBOURINE: takes its cue from the cymbals. A resonant wooden tray (or similar) must be held in one hand, while the fingers of the other beat out a suitable *rat-a-tat-tat.*
GLOCKENSPIEL: dinner bells, gong or chime would fill this demanding (though not to be taken too literally) part to perfection. Failing that, a heavy spanner, poker or other suitable metal (blunt) instrument hung on string should be sensitively tinkled with a small stick.
CASTANETS: small wooden box played with a hard beater, halved walnut shells or any resonant sticks or bones. This part is easy to improvise to great effect: like the tambourine in this piece, it takes its cue from the cymbals.
TRUMPET: the 'instrumentalist' should be taught his simple but most effective part from the piano. A brilliant ensemble is attained when the trumpeter hums his part through comb-and-paper: in a military manner, of course.
THE CHORUS: this is written in four parts, for Soprano, Alto, Tenor and Bass. At the very least everybody must sing something (if only to the note G which is easy to learn from the piano); inexperienced party-goers can be more easily taught to sing in parts than is generally supposed.

Having assisted the conductor to teach the orchestra its respective parts, the Pianist's duty is to improvise a fantasia introducing these captive and willing forces, or to lead from the given piano score. Each cue lasts at least two bars; performers who miss them even after rehearsal may be called upon to pay a forfeit.

Tempo has not been indicated, for this depends on the agility of the players. It must be carefully judged: not too funereal, but not on the other hand too fast for the impulsive soloists. Each player should have his own copy, and five minutes' rehearsal proves inestimable help. It lasts about five minutes and, 'given as a humorous interlude in an entertainment . . . will create hiliarious merriment.'

ORGAN.
HARP.
f
pp
f
pp
f
VIOLIN.
pp
TROMBONE.
f
FLUTE.
CYMBALS.
VIOLIN.
CHORUS.
Hip-hip-hur-rah! Hip-hip-hur-rah!
TROMBONE.
ff
pp
ff
pp
DRUM.
f
DRUM & HARP.
8va
loco.

TRUMPET.
f
ff TUTTI.
mp
p
TRUMPET, in Bass.
f
CYMBALS.
DRUM in Bass.
CHORUS.
Hip - hip-hur - rah !
Hip - hip-hur - rah !
GLOCKENSPIEL.
BAGPIPES.
FLUTE & ORGAN.
8va
ff TUTTI.
TROMBONE.
False alarms.
CHORUS.
Hip - hip-hur-rah ! Hip-hip-hur-rah !
ff TUTTI.

Musical Games for Winter Evenings
BY CLEMENT A·HARRIS·
Answers on page 112
This is a nest--find what is in it.
8va
Find three animals:
Find an insect, two birds, and a serpent:
Play or sing this:
Find four kinds of fish:
Some of the animals were partly
on
The man who caught the animals carried a
in his
and kept most of
them in a
which had
The

1. A Christmas Invitation.
and
2. The Acceptance.
Not I will in
ROUND
See Fa - ther Christ - mas sit - ting on a stool,
Warm - ing his hands at the bla - zing yule;
Wrapt in his cloak from head to chin, To
keep cold with - out and warmth with - - in!

So to the ending of the year. Though the introduction to this descriptive fantasia is reminiscent of Chopin's Funeral March, perhaps the composer had the demise of the Old Year in mind. Graham Ford's piece features the cake-walk, here an imitation of one of Scott Joplin's popular melodies. It has even the midnight chimes, but instead of *Auld Lang Syne*, which had not yet become an indispensable accompaniment to bidding the old year farewell, there is *Come, Lasses and Lads*, an irresistible invitation to dance the New Year in.

A Merry Party.
f
Ped.
1st time.
2nd time.
The Dance.
mf
ten.
ten.
ten.
ff
1st time.
2nd time.
mf
Games.
Allegro. 1st time f, 2nd time 8va.
Watching the Old Year out.
f Slow.
12 o'clock midnight.
Moderato.
1 2 3 4 5 6 7 8 9 10 11 12
Bells.
Ringing in the New Year.
ten.
ten.
ten.
Kind wishes.
Come, lasses and lads.
f Allegro giojoso.

Finale.
ff
ff
Ped.
FINE.
ff

ACKNOWLEDGMENTS AND PHOTOGRAPHIC CREDITS

I would particularly like to acknowledge my gratitude to the Editor of this book, Clive Unger-Hamilton and the Designer, Judith Allan for their expert assistance, tolerance and limitless expertise. R.G. 1980

Page
1 "Christmas Pleasures and Annoyances" *c.* 1856 *The Mansell Collection*
2 Christmas card, late 19th Century *The Mansell Collection*
3 "Pulling a Cracker" from Graphic 1878 *Mary Evans Picture Library*
7 Christmas Cards *c.* 1882 from drawings by C. J. Stanliand *The Mansell Collection*
8 "CountryWaits" *c.* 1850 *Mary Evans Picture Library*
8/9 "Family at the Piano" *c.* 1885 *Mary Evans Picture Library*
9 "Harmony" *c.* 1888 from Little Folk *George Sharp*
10 "Stirring the Christmas Pudding" from a picture by Henry Wood *c.* 1881 *The Mansell Collection*
11 (top left) "Winter Freuden" *The Mansell Collection*
(top right) "Pray God Bless" from All round the Clock *c.* 1880 *Mary Evans Picture Library*
12 "Scene at a Station" *c.* 1864 *Mary Evans Picture Library*
15 "A Boy's Dream of the coming Christmas" from picture by Adrien Marie *The Mansell Collection*
16 "Snowed up – Innocent Indoor Recreations – Music, Flirtations etc" Randolph Caldecott. The Graphic Christmas Number 1881 *Mary Evans Picture Library*
22 "The Mistletoe Bough" from The Girl's Own Paper *c.* 1880 *The Mansell Collection*
28 (left) "The Song of the Robin Redbreast" Music cover *Richard Graves*

Page

(bottom right) "Feeding Robins" *c.* 1880 *Mary Evans Picture Library*
29 "Bringing Home the Christmas Tree" 1882 by A. Hunt *The Mansell Collection*
30 "The Mistletoe Seller" by Phiz from the Illustrated London News 1853 *Mary Evans Picture Library*
35 Two illustrations from the Curmudgeon's Christmas by Randolph Caldecott *c.* 1880 *George Sharp*
37 "The Village Choir rehearsing the Christmas Anthem" ...... drawn by A. Hunt – December 1863 *Peter Newark's Historical Pictures*
38 Two Victorian Christmas cards *c.* 1880 *The Mansell Collection* and *George Sharp*
40 "The toy shop" by Thomas Benjamin Kennington *Sotheby's Belgravia*
42 Victorian Christmas Card *c.* 1880 *George Sharp*
43 "A Workman's Home – Rose and Crown Court, Islington" 1875 *Mary Evans Picture Library*
46 "Returning from Christmas Drill" 1860 *The Mansell Collection*
48 From Cassells Family Magazine *c.* 1877 *George Sharp*
49 "A Visit to the Old Folk on Christmas Eve" drawn by A Hunt. The Illustrated London News 1864 *The Mansell Collection*
51 "The Norfolk Coach at Christmas" by R. Seymour 1836 *The Mansell Collection*
52 "Snowballing on Christmas Eve" The Illustrated London News 1880 *Mary Evans Picture Library*
57 (left) "Wie der Weihnachtsmann" *Mary Evans Picture Library*
(right) "Snapdragon" drawn by Gabriel Nicolet *Mary Evans Picture Library*
59 (top) "The Christmas Tree" by J. A. Pasquier. The Illustrated London News 1858 *Peter Newark's Historical Pictures*
(bottom) Music Cover "A Christmas Pary" *Richard Graves*
67 (left) "Holly Boughs" by M. E. Edwards *Mary Evans Picture Library*
(right) "A Child's Christmas Memories" by Mrs. Staples *c.* 1883 *The Mansell Collection*
71 (left) "Christmas Grotesques" 1879 by Ernest Griset *The Mansell Collection*
(right) "The Christmas Pudding" by R. Seymour *c.* 1830 *The Mansell Collection*
74 "High Life below Stairs" by Robert Cruikshank *The Mansell Collection*
77 "Don't Cousin Charlie!" drawn by F. Barnard. The Illustrated London News 1875 *The Mansell Collection*
78 Illustration from the Curmudgeon's Christmas by Randolph Caldecott *c.* 1880 *George Sharp*
80 Tail Piece from Home Notes December 1895 *George Sharp*
81 (left) "The Spirit of Pantomime" from Theatre Royal, Drury Lane Christmas 1895 Pantomime – Cinderella *Richard Graves*
(right) Drury Lane Pantomime from The Visit to London 1902 *Mary Evans Picture Library*
84 (left) "The Fairy Godmother" from Theatre Royal, Drury Lane Christmas 1895 Pantomime – Cinderella. *Richard Graves*
(right) "The Cross Dwarf" from Little Folks *c.* 1880 *George Sharp*
85 Christmas card *c.* 1860 *Mary Evans Picture Library*
89 "The Bride" from Theatre Royal, Drury Lane Christmas 1895 Pantomime – Cinderella *Richard Graves*
91 Tail Piece from Home Notes December 1895 *George Sharp*
92 "Dreaming of Christmas" from a Christmas Tree Fairy *c.* 1890 *Mary Evans Picture Library*
95 "One often sees the Cotillon begun in a clear sunlight". Harpers New Monthly Magazine 1894 *Peter Newark's Historical Pictures*
96 "The Road – Winter" Currier & Ives print 1853 *Peter Newark's Historical Pictures*
107 Illustration from the Curmudgeon's Christmas by Randolph Caldecott *c.* 1880 *George Sharp*
110 "Dancing in the New Year – A Welcome to 1873" by Arthur Boyd Houghton in Graphic *Mary Evans Picture Library*
111 "The Last Night of the Mistletoe" by J. Godwin 1859 *George Sharp*

ANSWERS

1 Four eggs.
2 Gee-gee; Hyena (high E-na); Dog.
3 Bee; Cuckoo; Tern (turn); Boa.
4 Dace; Flat (fish); Bass; Cod.
5 Some of the animals were partly *Fed* on *Cabbage*.
6 The man who caught the animals carried a *Staff* in his *Baggage* and kept most of them in a *Cage* which had *Bars*. The *End*.

A Christmas Invitation: *One, sharp. Beef and Cabbage.*
The Acceptance: *Not a bad feed. Naturally* (natural E) *I will be in time.*